GOLF NUTS

LO LINKERT

ISBN 0-929097-00-9

LO-BOY GOLFTOONS NORTH AMERICA INC.
500 Capitol of Texas Hwy.
Building 3, Suite 200
Austin, Texas
78746

#1-8307 – 124th St.
Surrey, B.C., Canada
V3W 9G2

GOLF NUTS

How often have you heard non-golfing friends say "You've got to be nuts to chase a little white ball"? I was guilty of that attitude myself 25 years ago. I just didn't believe that intelligent and often famous people took up this nutty game of golf and got hooked on it.

A quarter of a century ago I was working as an illustrator for one of Canada's largest retail stores. When I heard that a company golf tournament was being held the next day and all employees who entered would have a day off, that was motivation enough for me. Feeling like a caged in squirrel, I welcomed the opportunity of getting out of the office for a wonderful sunny day on the links. Never having played golf before in my life, the only problem was how to become a golfer in 24 hours. I signed up for the tournament never suspecting that this heroic step was to change my whole life. The evening before the tournament, a good friend took me to a driving range and taught me how to hold a club and how to swing and miss the ball. Believe it or not, my very first (and for a long time, best) golf shot was 150 yards right down the middle! That was followed by at least ten ego destroying whiffs. After two more buckets of balls and four bleeding blisters on my left hand, I felt sure I would be a tough competitor for tomorrow's tournament. Setting out with a fifty year old set of clubs and a golf bag which smelled like an old potato sack, I marched to the tee with blind courage; I also swung at the ball like a blind man. Taking a 13 on the first hole, I had opened the golden gate for myself to a wonderful future of golf, though I didn't know it then. I was the first man on the green and thought that must be worth something until my three partners asked me what was my hurry. I had received no instructions in the etiquette or rules of golf but by the second hole I was an expert and waited my turn. We were playing a four ball best ball game and I must admit I was the weakest link in the chain. I added only one point to my teams effort. I was a little depressed and began to believe that the two hundred balls at the driving range the night before were totally wasted. The only excuse I had left was my bleeding blisters and four bandages on my left hand. I finished with a 135 and when my score was transferred to a score sheet outside of the Pro Shop, the laughter of the scorekeeper went through me like a poisoned dart. I figured I had no business taking part in the big banquet scheduled for that evening, so I quietly snuck around the building to my car and called it a day. My boss asked the next morning what time it was and I told him it was high time to realize that golf isn't for me and that it was 10:15. "Too bad you have a watch already" he said. He told me I had won an $80.00 wristwatch the night before for being the hardest worker! Now I had to prove something to them and to myself.

My addiction was born. I was hooked for life on this nutty game called golf. Since golf is the most humorous game in the world and my dream was to become a fulltime cartoonist, I killed two birdies with one pen.

This book will give you an inside look at the humorous side of golf. You don't have to be a golfer to laugh with me but if you are or even if you just know a golfer, you will feel with me. I am now a ten handicapper and a fulltime cartoonist. My wife Inge is also an ardent golfer and a critic of my cartoons. Every sunny day we spend on the golf course and enjoy life to the fullest. If there is such a thing as reincarnation, all I want is a repeat of this life.

"SIR, ARE THOSE LONG-SHORT PANTS, OR SHORT-LONG PANTS?"

3

THIS IS A $ 250.000 PUTT, WHICH IS WATCHED BY 10 MILLION PEOPLE AROUND THE WORLD, INCLUDING ALL YOUR SPONSORS, PLUS THE I.R.S."

"IF YOU DRIVE YOUR CAR, LIKE YOU DRIVE ME, WE'RE BOTH IN TROUBLE!"

"DO YOU GUYS REALIZE THAT WE SPEND ONE-THIRD OF OUR LIVES IN BED AND THE OTHER TWO THIRDS IN THE ROUGH?"

1 2

3

4

7　　　　　8

"HEY FELLOWS COME HERE, ANDY INVESTED IN A BRAND NEW BALL."

7

8

"... AND PLEASE FORGIVE ME FOR MY LANGUAGE I USED ON THE GOLF COURSE WITH YOU, BEFORE I FOUND OUT YOU WERE A PRIEST."

"NO, SIR, WE DON'T MIND YOU PLAYING THROUGH, GO RIGHT AHEAD."

DAD, HAPPY DAY'S ARE HERE AGAIN...WE MADE A BUNDLE, YOUR GOLF CLUBS ALONE BROUGHT $ 29.00."

E TOLD YOU ONCE, I TOLD YOU A MILLION TIMES, KEEP
OUR HEAD DOWN, STAY CLOSER TO THE FISH AND FOLLOW
THROUGH!"

"... AND IF YOUR HUSBAND WAS A GOLFER ...."

"DO YOU KNOW TODAY IS FRIDAY THE 13th?"

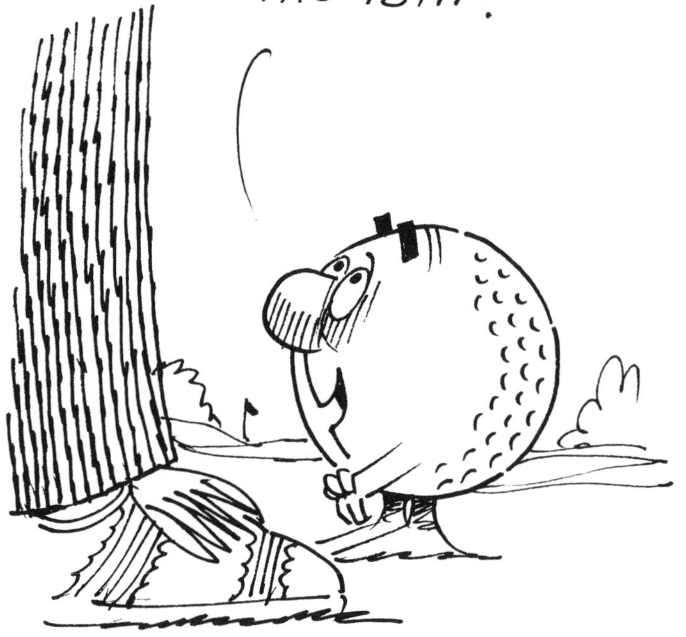

"I'M SORRY, I MAKE IT MY POLICY NEVER TO LEND MY GOLF-CLUBS TO ANYONE UNDER 90 YEARS AND ONLY THEN IF HE'S A SCRATCH GOLFER!"

27

"YOU'RE ASKING ME WHAT YOU DID WRONG ..... EVERYTHING!"

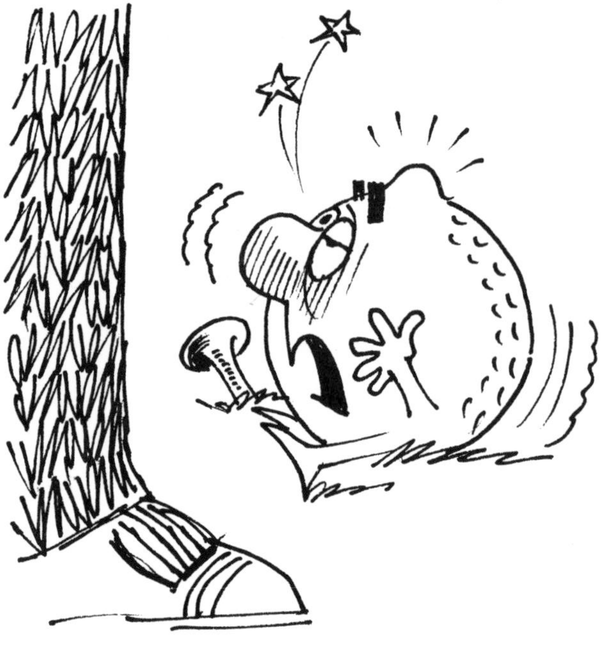

"NO M'AM HE ISN'T HERE...OH NOW I SEE HIM, HE'S HAVING A HARD TIME IN THE KITTY-LITTER."

WELL, IN GOLFER'S LANGUAGE I'D CALL IT A SUDDEN DEATH."

"HOLD IT RIGHT THERE, SONNY, YOU'RE IN THE WRONG GAME!"

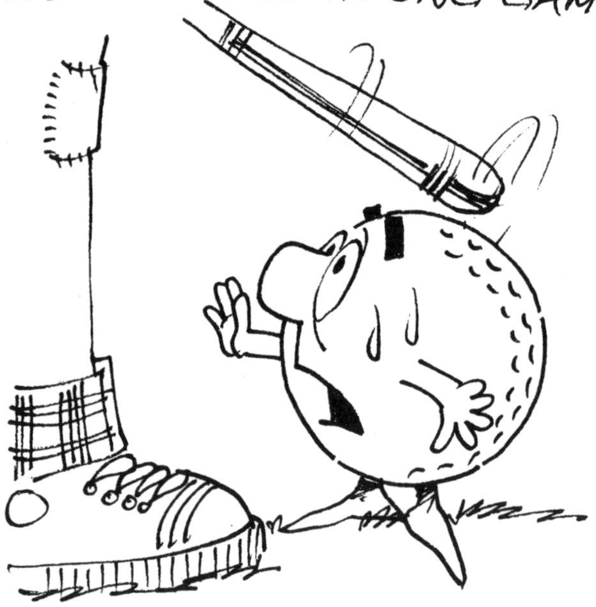

HURRY UP, DAD, THE THREE SANDBAGGERS ARE HERE!'"

"E SHOULD'VE TAKEN HIS CHEST PAIN'S SERIOUSLY AND NOT
EFT HIM BEHIND ON THE SECOND HOLE SO WE COULD FINISH THE GAME."

"IS IT TRUE THAT 'RED' BALLS HAVE A LEANING TO THE LEFT?"

" UP--UP-- I SAID UP!!! "

"NO SIR, YOUR LUGGAGE ARRIVED SAFELY, JUST YOUR GOLF CLUBS WENT TO BULGARIA."

" REFRESH MY MEMORY, WALTER, WAS THAT A 69 I SHOT TODAY, OR A 169 ? "

"AND IF HE DOESN'T FLINCH WHEN YOU TELL HIM YOU HAD A PAR, SAY SORRY, I MEAN A BIRDIE."

HOW DO YOU EVER EXPECT TO BECOME A SUCCESSFUL CADDIE IF YOU DON'T EVEN KNOW HOW TO FLATTER A BIG TIPPER.!? "

I'M NOT GOING TO CLIMB UP ON THIS TEE UNTIL YOU TAKE BACK THAT TERRIBLE NAME YOU JUST CALLED ME!"

"AND A GET-WELL CARD FROM THE GUY WHO HIT YOU. HE'D LIKE TO KNOW IF YOU SAW WHAT DIRECTION HIS BALL RICOCHETED."

49

OH, BOY, I SHOULD'VE GONE TO CHURCH INSTEAD!"

51

1   **2**

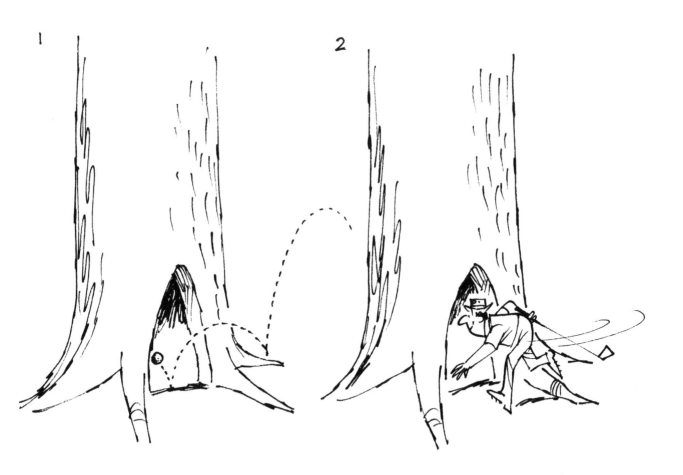

3

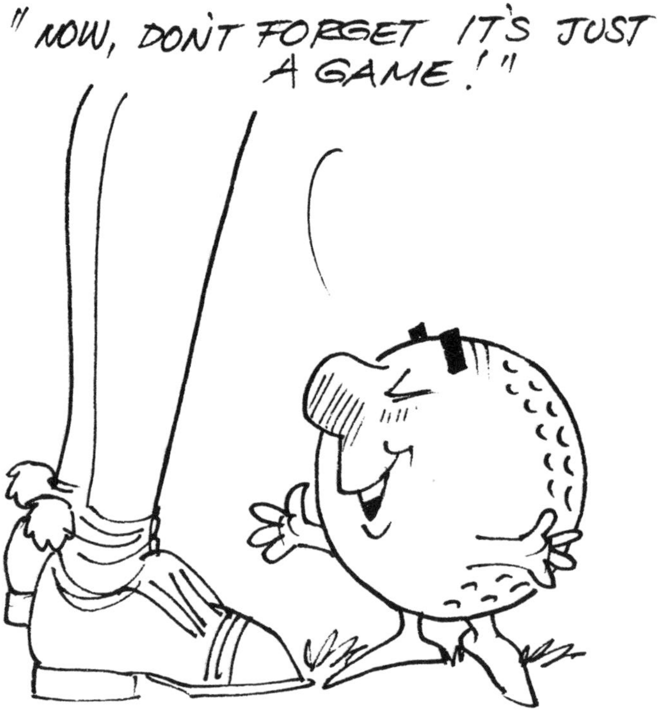
"NOW, DON'T FORGET IT'S JUST A GAME!"

"MY GRANDMOTHER CAN HIT A MEATBALL TWICE AS FAR WITH A BROOMSTICK!"

55

"I'M CUTTING DOWN ON MY PUTTING, I ALLOW MYSELF ONLY TWO POTTS PER HOLE!"

5

6

"HE'S A REAL ANIMAL ... 150 YARDS EVERY TIME!"

"DO ME A FAVOR, HENRY, AND STOP HUMMING 'FEELINGS'!"

"SINCE I MET THE HUMAN I LOVE
THE ANIMAL!"

"I DIDN'T SAY YOU HAVE A FUNNY FIGURE, ALL I SAID WAS YOU HAVE A FUNNY WAY WITH FIGURES!"

2

3

"WOULD YOU GENTLEMEN MIND IF WE GO AHEAD OF YOU, THIS IS OUR VERY FIRST GAME."

"SHUSH, GIRLS, I'M JUST CHECKING THE LIST OF NO-NO'S THE PRO GAVE ME!"

71

"WHAT DO YOU MEAN 'VERY FUNNY' IT WOULDN'T BE THE FIRST TIME YOU BLEW ME INTO THIS LAKE!"

THREE ANGRY MEN ON THE FIRST TEE WANT A WORD WITH YOU."

"I WOULD GIVE YOU A HAND, HONEY, BUT I'VE GOT A TEE-OFF TIME FOR TWO PM."

"VERY FUNNY!"

"..THEN ONE DAY I SAID TO MY-SELF WHAT CAN I DO THAT THOSE HACKERS CAN'T FIND ME ANYMORE."

"SOMEBODY UP THERE DOESN'T LIKE YOU!"

" SORRY MR. HOPKINS, YOUR FAMILY MOVED ABOUT SIX MONTHS AGO. "

81

CHAMPAGNE FOR THE HOUSE... I BROKE THE 'HUNDRED' TODAY,
...AND IT TOOK ME ONLY 7 HOLES TO DO IT!"

"NO THANKS, HONEY, I'LL WALK, I HAVE TO CONCENTRATE ON MY GAME!"

" NOT MUCH ... WATCHING 'MISSION IMPOSSIBLE. "

" HERE'S MY PLAN ! "

"DROP THE BAG CADDIE, DROP IT!!!"

91

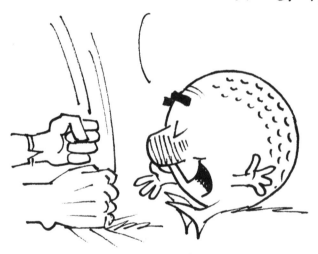

"HERE COMES THE ODD COUPLE, HE'S A BIG SLICER AND SHE'S ON THE OPPOSITE SIDE OF THE FAIRWAY."

"OH, NO! THEY TOLD ME DOWN THERE YOU CANT TAKE YOUR CLUBS WITH YOU!"

Golfers – ENOUGH IS ENOUGH!

GO AHEAD, MAKE MY SEASON!

'Dimples' the humanized golfball is Lo's creation and success story. A hilarious book about the long suffering golfball. All golfers will be able to sympathize with and relate to Dimples and his plight. Every golfer will enjoy this book - at the 19th hole, the locker room, or in the comfort of an easy chair by the fire.

2 MORE HITS OF GOLF CARTOON BOOKS

GOLF EPIDEMIC

LO LINKERT

This book is written in the international 'language of Golf', without captions. A rib tickling look at the misfortunes of golfers of all ages. All golfers, no matter what their language, age, or handicap will find themselves in these pages.

1990 GOLF-TOON CALENDAR

Golf Calendars — in full colour. Each cartoon is vibrant and bright and suitable for framing. A sure hit for all golfing enthusiasts — to be enjoyed every day of the year.

Look for these items and other Lo-Boy Golftoon items in your favorite bookstore, pro shop or gift shop, or write to the publisher

LO-BOY GOLFTOONS OF NORTH AMERICA INC.
500 Capitol of Tx Hwy.
Building 3 - Suite 200
Austin, Texas
USA, 78746

IN CANADA:
#1-8307 - 124th Street
Surrey, British Columbia
Canada, V3W 9G2